CONFRONTATION

SPAWN

SPAWN®: CONFRONTATION
ISBN 1 85286 832 5

Published by Titan Books Ltd
42 - 44 Dolben St
London SE1 0UP
In association with Image Comics™

This book collects issues 21 – 25 of the Image Comics' series *Spawn*.

British Library Cataloguing-In-Publication data. A catalogue record for this
book is available from the British Library.

First edition: September 1997
10 9 8 7 6 5 4 3 2 1

Printed in Italy.

CONFRONTATION

SPAWN ®

TODD McFARLANE
With MARC SILVESTRI and GREG CAPULLO

TITAN BOOKS
in association with IMAGE COMICS ™

Like some infernal Grand Master, poised over a chessboard on which damned souls line up against the forces of light, the demon lord Malebolgia surveys his opening gambit and brays a mirthless, rasping cackle.

Idly, he runs a razored talon down the mottled, scarred figure that stands at forefront of his stygian strategy, admiring the handiwork that has wrought such glorious agony and mouth-watering despair. This is his Hellspawn, his knight errant. This is the general who will lead his forces to the doors of Heaven itself and tear them asunder.

Once this Spawn was a man. Flawed and already partway to his own damnation, but at heart noble and loyal. Perfect raw material to lead the Army of Darkness.

Al Simmons was his name. A solider in clandestine wars fought behind a veil of lies and twilit secrecy, a good man with too much blood on his hands to ever completely wash away. A family man too, deeply in love with and devoted to his wife Wanda. And there lay his fatal flaw, the emotional trap that would prove his undoing.

Murdered by his own colleague Chapel, a minor pawn employed merely as a distraction to mask more subtle moves, Simmons descended to Hell, his soul now the clay for the sculptor of sinners.

Re-made, moulded into a being of arcane power and clothed in a suit of living necroplasm, the fledgling Spawn blindly accepted Malebolgia's offer, discarding all common sense in return

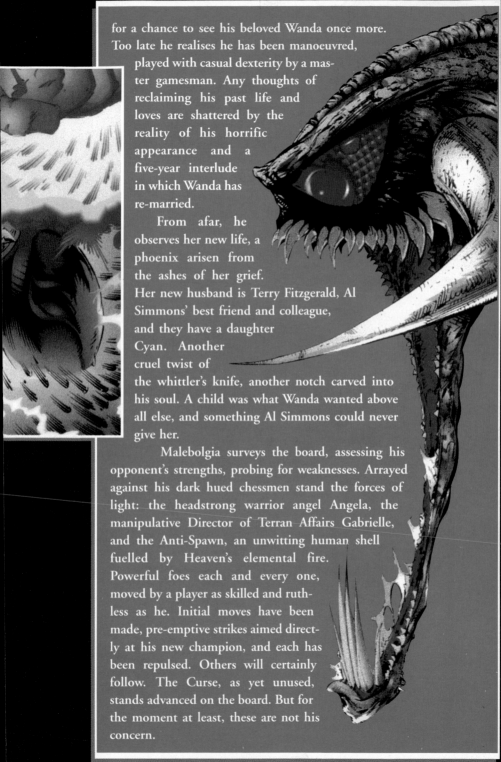

for a chance to see his beloved Wanda once more. Too late he realises he has been manoeuvred, played with casual dexterity by a master gamesman. Any thoughts of reclaiming his past life and loves are shattered by the reality of his horrific appearance and a five-year interlude in which Wanda has re-married.

From afar, he observes her new life, a phoenix arisen from the ashes of her grief. Her new husband is Terry Fitzgerald, Al Simmons' best friend and colleague, and they have a daughter Cyan. Another cruel twist of the whittler's knife, another notch carved into his soul. A child was what Wanda wanted above all else, and something Al Simmons could never give her.

Malebolgia surveys the board, assessing his opponent's strengths, probing for weaknesses. Arrayed against his dark hued chessmen stand the forces of light: the headstrong warrior angel Angela, the manipulative Director of Terran Affairs Gabrielle, and the Anti-Spawn, an unwitting human shell fuelled by Heaven's elemental fire. Powerful foes each and every one, moved by a player as skilled and ruthless as he. Initial moves have been made, pre-emptive strikes aimed directly at his new champion, and each has been repulsed. Others will certainly follow. The Curse, as yet unused, stands advanced on the board. But for the moment at least, these are not his concern.

Players from other games, played in parallel with, or tangential to, the main board, intrude and distract, mounting their own cross-challenge to his champion.

Chief among them, the mob boss Tony Twist and Simmons' one-time employer Jason Wynn. The former, seeking revenge for the bloody murder of several of his lieutenants, an act perpetrated by the Malebolgia's own straying gamepiece The Violator. The latter, seeking to regain face in the wake of his abduction and transformation into the Anti-Spawn. Both moving in different directions, closing pincer-like in on Spawn.

Secondary, though no less imminent or dangerous, threats come in the shape of Overt-Kill, a murderous cyborg employed by Tony Twist, and NYPD detectives Sam Burke and 'Twitch' Williams, two cops with no love for loose cannons like Spawn and a tenacious habit of running their suspect to ground.

Malebolgia considers. Should he interfere, advance players of his own to counter the threats? No, let his champion prove his mettle in this coming confrontation, let the flames of conflict forge his armour. For in the end, those fires, drawn from the depths of Hell itself, will bind Spawn to him irrevocably. And then, the game will be his.

Still, thinks Malebolgia, perhaps one pawn could be sacrificed. And with a second malicious peal of laughter, Terry Fitzgerald is placed exposed and alone on the board...

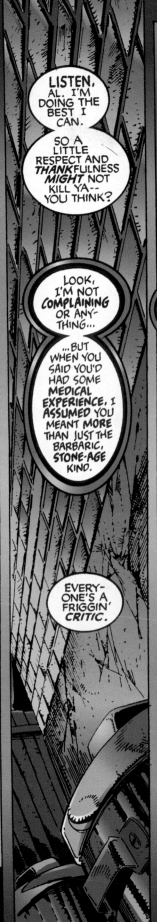

SLAM!

TESTY LITTLE CREEP.

ANYWAYS...

I'M LOOKING FORWARD TO A *GREAT* WEEK. SMITHERS, BRING ME UP TO DATE.

AS YOU KNOW, SIR, WE'VE BEEN LOOKING FOR LINKS BETWEEN THE MURDERS OF YOUR ASSOCIATES AND SOME OTHER DISRUPTIVE SITUATIONS... THE MATTER OF THAT LITTLE FAT *CLOWN*, THE DISMANTLING OF THAT HIRED GUN *OVERT-KILL*, AND THE INVASION OF YOUR OFFICE BY A *COSTUMED VIGILANTE.*

CALLING IN *THE ADMONISHER* TO DEAL WITH THE CLOWN WAS A BRILLIANT MOVE, SIR.*

I APPRECIATE THAT.

WE'RE HAVING TO DO A LITTLE DIGGING ON THE LATTER TWO INCIDENTS.

SORTING OUT THE *CLOWN'S* KILLING SPREE HAS BEEN EASIER. THERE'S NO QUESTION HE CARRIED OUT THE HITS ON THE OTHER DONS, AND THAT HE ACTED ALONE.

*VIOLATOR #1 -- Tom.

CONTINUE.

REGARDING THE *OVERT-KILL* SITUATION, WE HAVE SOME NEW LEADS.

WE HAD DRAWINGS MADE OF THE WEAPONS YOU DESCRIBED, AS USED BY THE COSTUMED INVADER.*

OUR PEOPLE AT THE F.B.I. AND C.I.A. BOTH CONFIRM THE THEFT OF THOSE WEAPONS. THE FIREPOWER WAS EASILY SUFFICIENT TO PIERCE OVERT-KILL'S ARMOR.

HE'S *TERENCE FITZGERALD,* AN OPERATIVE FOR SOME ULTRA-COVERT AGENCY.

IT TOOK SOME ARM-TWISTING, BUT WE GOT A NAME FOR A SUSPECT... SOMEONE WHO SEEMS TO HAVE STICKY FINGERS FOR CONFIDENTIAL FILES, AS WELL.

GET ME EVERYTHING YOU CAN ON HIM.

*ISSUE #6.

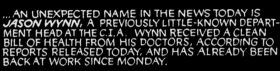

... AN UNEXPECTED NAME IN THE NEWS TODAY IS *JASON WYNN*, A PREVIOUSLY LITTLE-KNOWN DEPARTMENT HEAD AT THE *C.I.A.* WYNN RECEIVED A CLEAN BILL OF HEALTH FROM HIS DOCTORS, ACCORDING TO REPORTS RELEASED TODAY, AND HAS ALREADY BEEN BACK AT WORK SINCE MONDAY.

HE UNDERWENT SOME SIXTY PHYSICAL AND PSYCHO-LOGICAL TESTS AFTER BEING DISCOVERED CRUMPLED ON HIS OFFICE FLOOR THE PREVIOUS FRIDAY. THERE ARE STILL FEW DETAILS REGARDING HIS ABSENCE WEDNESDAY AND THURSDAY OF LAST WEEK, THOUGH ABDUCTION BY A HOSTILE AGENCY HAS NOT BEEN RULED OUT.

WYNN *CLAIMS* NO RECOLLECTION OF ANYTHING THAT OCCURED DURING HIS ABSENCE. ACCORDING TO A *WITNESS*, THE DIRECTOR WAS SPIRITED MYSTERIOUSLY OUT OF A C.I.A. GYMNASIUM. THE DISAPPEARANCE LED TO AN EXHAUSTIVE SEARCH WHICH ENDED WHEN A NIGHT CUSTODIAN FOUND HIM. APPARENTLY, WYNN HAD SOMEHOW RETURNED UNDETECTED TO HIS OWN PRIVATE OFFICE ON THE TENTH FLOOR, WHICH WAS LOCKED FROM THE OUTSIDE.

WHAT HAS DOCTORS CONCERNED IS WYNN'S UNEXPLAINABLE PARA-AMNESIA. REPEATED PROBES AND C.A.T. SCANS OF THE DIRECTOR'S BRAIN AND CENTRAL NERVOUS SYSTEM HAS REVEALED NO INDICATIONS OF PHYSICAL TRAUMA OR INVASIVE MANIPULATION OF ANY SORT.

A HOSPITAL SPOKESPERSON, SPEAKING ON CONDITION OF ANONYMITY, EMPHASIZED THAT THERE IS NO SIGN OF INJURY WHATSOEVER AND THAT WYNN IS IN TOP PHYSICAL HEALTH. HOWEVER, HE WILL CONTINUE TO BE TESTED OVER THE NEXT SEVERAL WEEKS IN CASE SIMILAR SYMPTOMS ARISE.

WYNN WAS UNAVAILABLE FOR COMMENT, BUT HIS PERSONAL AIDE HAS RELATED THAT MR. WYNN IS BACK TO WORK *"IN FULL FORCE"* AND PROCEEDING AS IF THE ENTIRE EVENT NEVER OCCURED. THE C.I.A., N.S.A. AND N.S.C. ALL HAD NO COMMENT BUT THAT MR. WYNN IS BEING WATCHED CLOSELY FOR ANY *SIGNS* OF FUTURE ABNORMALITY.

GREAT DAY IN THE MORNING! LET'S GO OVER THE FACTS, IF THE C.I.A. DOESN'T MIND. A MEMBER OF THEIR *DIRECTORATE* DISAPPEARS, ala *'STAR TREK,"* APPARENTLY OFF THE FACE OF THE *EARTH,* AND THEN JUST SHOWS UP TWO DAYS LATER, THUMB IN HIS MOUTH, HUDDLED IN A FETAL BALL IN HIS OFFICE. HE REMEMBERS *SQUAT,* BUT THAT'S OKAY, 'CAUSE HE'S ONE OF THE GOOD OL' BOYS. SO, THEY GET HIM TO PEE IN A CUP, A DOZEN TOP-SECURITY DOCTORS WRITE UP A DOZEN UNREADABLE REPORTS, AND THEY SEND HIM BACK TO WORK WITH AN APPLE IN HIS LUNCH-BOX. AT THE SAME TIME, THEY DECLARE IT *MIGHT* HAVE BEEN AN ENEMY ACTION AND YET DON'T BLINK AN EYE AT THE POSSIBILITY OUR TOP-SECRET BOY SCOUT IS *COMPROMISED!*

WAS HE KIDNAPPED OR *WASN'T* HE? PERHAPS HE WAS OFF IN ARUBA WITH MISS MONEYPENNY-- OUR TAX PENNIES AT WORK! I BET IF YOU OR I TRIED THIS CRAP WE'D BE WALKING THE STREETS IN TEN SECONDS FLAT. I KNOW *I'LL* SLEEP BETTER KNOWING THAT BOYS LIKE THIS ARE IN CHARGE OF OUR *NATIONAL SECURITY!*

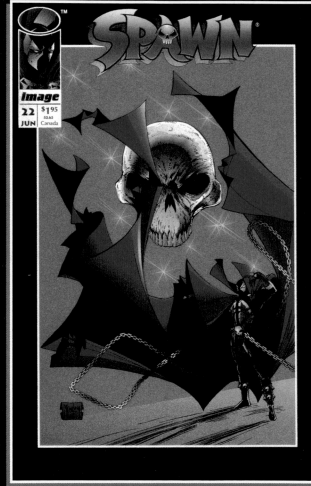

PREDICTABLE.

THAT'S BECOME THE ESSENCE OF JOE SACIK'S LIFE. THE 15-HOUR WORK DAYS HAVE BECOME ROUTINE.

INDEED, JOE SACIK IS A LOYAL SERVANT OF THE MOB.

THAT TRUST IS AN EXHAUSTIVELY HEAVY BURDEN. AS HEAD OF ACCOUNTING, JOE HAS TO KEEP TABS ON ALL DETAILS OF TONY TWIST'S BUSINESS ACTIVITIES.

INFORMATION IS GATHERED. ORGANIZED. SANITIZED. CAREFULLY ACCOUNTED FOR. AN AUDIT WOULD SHOW A CLEAN, LEGAL OPERATION.

SKRITCH
SKRITCH
SKRITCH

SO JOE LABORS TOWARD THAT END, KEENLY FIDDLING ALL THE BOSS' DEALINGS INTO CLEAR HARMONY.

NO SOCIAL LIFE.

NO LOVE INTERESTS.

NO FRIENDS.

IN RETURN, HE HAS BEEN REWARDED WITH THE COMPLETE TRUST OF HIS BOSS--

--TONY TWIST.

MAINTAINING THAT SHELL OF LEGITIMACY IS A MUST.

MAYBE TOO MUCH.

THE HIGHEST PRIORITY.

ALL THE PIECES ARE EVENTUALLY RELEVANT, AND THUS HE HAS ACCESS TO EVERY BIT OF DATA.

?

AS FOR **JOE SAKIC**, THREE DAYS FROM NOW, HIS BODY WILL BE FOUND UNDER THE GEORGE WASHINGTON BRIDGE, WITH HIS HANDS AND FEET VICIOUSLY SEVERED. DECAPITATED. EVEN HIS GENITALS WILL BE MISSING.

THE POLICE WILL CONDUCT A FULL INVESTIGATION, BUT IN THE ABSENCE OF ANYTHING IDENTIFIABLE ABOUT THE BODY, WILL HAVE TO CLOSE THE CASE OF **JOHN DOE 1994-714**.

SUCH IS THE LIFE OF A TRUSTED EMPLOYEE OF TONY TWIST.

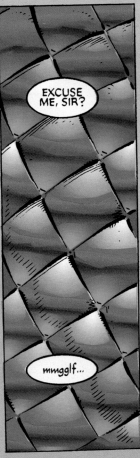

EXCUSE ME, SIR?

mmgglf...

JUST GOT OFF THE PHONE WITH OUR SNITCH, JIMMY. SEEMS HE'S BEEN DOING HIS HOMEWORK.

ONE OF THE BUMS HE KNOWS SAYS OUR HERO USUALLY HANGS OUT IN THE SAME FOUR BLOCK RADIUS.

I'VE MAPPED IT OUT ALREADY, SIR.

mmm-mMMm...

I'LL DO SOME EARLY SCOUTING AND ASK A FEW QUESTIONS.

MEET YOU AT PORT AUTHORITY AT 10 O'CLOCK.

OKAY, SIR?

SIR!

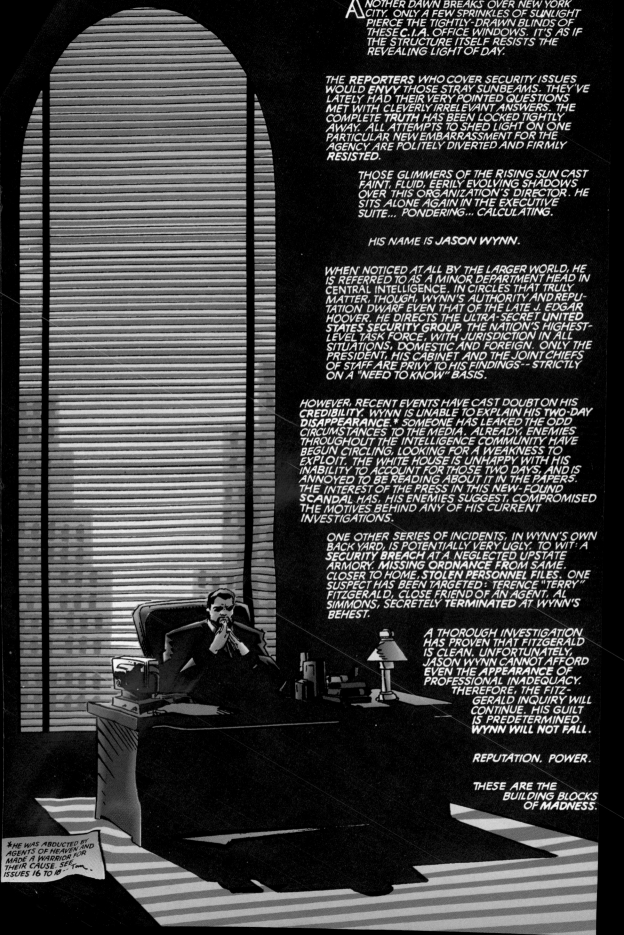

Another dawn breaks over New York City. Only a few sprinkles of sunlight pierce the tightly-drawn blinds of these C.I.A. office windows. It's as if the structure itself resists the revealing light of day.

The REPORTERS who cover security issues would ENVY those stray sunbeams. They've lately had their very pointed questions met with cleverly irrelevant answers. The complete TRUTH has been locked tightly away. All attempts to shed light on one particular new embarrassment for the agency are politely diverted and firmly resisted.

Those glimmers of the rising sun cast faint, fluid, eerily evolving shadows over this organization's director. He sits alone again in the executive suite... pondering... calculating.

His name is JASON WYNN.

When noticed at all by the larger world, he is referred to as a minor department head in Central Intelligence. In circles that truly matter, though, Wynn's authority and reputation dwarf even that of the late J. Edgar Hoover. He directs the ultra-secret United States Security Group, the nation's highest-level task force, with jurisdiction in all situations, domestic and foreign. Only the President, his cabinet and the joint chiefs of staff are privy to his findings-- strictly on a "need to know" basis.

However, recent events have cast doubt on his CREDIBILITY. Wynn is unable to explain his two-day DISAPPEARANCE.* Someone has leaked the odd circumstances to the media. Already, enemies throughout the intelligence community have begun circling, looking for a weakness to exploit. The White House is unhappy with his inability to account for those two days, and is annoyed to be reading about it in the papers. The interest of the press in this new-found SCANDAL has, his enemies suggest, compromised the motives behind any of his current investigations.

One other series of incidents, in Wynn's own back yard, is potentially very ugly. To wit: a SECURITY BREACH at a neglected upstate armory. MISSING ORDNANCE from same. Closer to home, STOLEN PERSONNEL FILES. One suspect has been targeted: Terence "Terry" Fitzgerald, close friend of an agent, Al Simmons, secretely terminated at Wynn's behest.

A thorough investigation has proven that Fitzgerald is clean. Unfortunately, Jason Wynn cannot afford even the APPEARANCE of professional inadequacy. Therefore, the Fitzgerald inquiry will continue. His guilt is predetermined. WYNN WILL NOT FALL.

REPUTATION. POWER.

These are the BUILDING BLOCKS OF MADNESS.

*He was abducted by agents of Heaven and made a warrior for their cause. See issues 16 to 18 --Tom

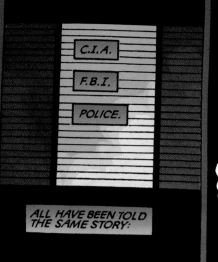

C.I.A.

F.B.I.

POLICE.

ALL HAVE BEEN TOLD THE SAME STORY:

...THAT ONE OF THEIR OWN HAS **TURNED** ON THEM. THE ACCUSATION COMES FROM SO HIGH UP THAT IT GOES **UNCHALLENGED.** MEANWHILE, "CONCRETE EVIDENCE" HAS BEEN MANUFACTURED, APPROPRIATE TO SATISFY ANYONE'S QUESTIONS.

MAN, WHAT A BORE!

I **HATE** FILLING OUT THESE DAMN REPORTS.

ESPECIALLY WHEN I HAVE TO FILL 'EM OUT IN **RUSSIAN.**

WHAT A PAIN.

TERRY FITZGERALD CONCENTRATES ON HIS MONITOR, TRYING TO FORGET THE HARRASSING **PHONE CALL** AND FACE-TO-FACE **THREATS.** PRACTICALLY EVERY LAW ENFORCEMENT OR INTELLIGENCE AGENCY IN THE STATE HAS MADE THEIR DISPLEASURE KNOWN.

HE IS GRATEFUL THAT WANDA IS UNAWARE OF THIS WITCH-HUNT. HIS FAMILY'S UNTOUCHED.

HE KNOWS THAT WON'T LAST.

COULD THE DEBACLE AT COLUMBIA UNIVERSITY* HAVE HAD SOMETHING TO DO WITH HIS PREDICAMENT? HE WAS NEVER CONFIDENT IN HIS FIELD ABILITIES-- WAS HE BEING **TESTED?** IF SO, IT WAS NO HELP WHEN THAT UKRANIAN NUCLEAR SCIENTIST--

JEE-ZUS!

EEEK!

*ISSUES 19 AND 20-- NOT OUT YET! -- Tom.

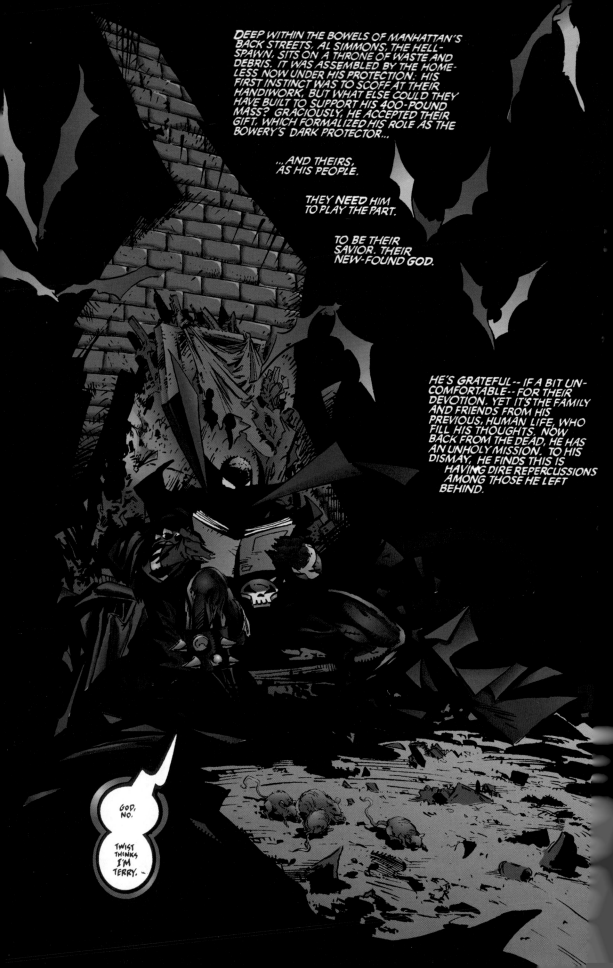

"...AND—AS YOU REQUESTED, MR. TWIST, AN ADDITIONAL CONTROL CIRCUIT HAS BEEN INSTALLED. IT WILL OVERRIDE ANY HOMING SIGNALS SENT OUT BY OUR OPPONENTS.

GOOD.

ADDITIONAL MODIFICATIONS WERE MADE TO HIS BARRIUM ARMOR. WHILE COMBAT DAMAGE TO HIS EXO-SKELETON IS ALWAYS POSSIBLE, THIS WILL KEEP IT MINIMAL.

THE SAME ASSAULTS USED IN THE PAST WOULD NOW BE RATHER USELESS.

EXCELLENT!

I KNEW I COULD COUNT ON YOU AND YOUR BOYS.

uh...

THERE IS *ONE* SLIGHT PROBLEM, SIR.

THAT BEING?

IT SEEMS WE WEREN'T ABLE TO COMPLETELY WIPE SOME OF HIS MEMORIES. THERE ARE A FEW IMPULSE-WAVES THAT INCLUDE DATA ON THE GOVERNMENT'S *YOUNG-BLOOD* TEAM THAT IGNORED OUR 'DELETE' COMMANDS.

DO I MAKE MYSELF CLEAR?

TONIGHT.

BZZT

I'M NOT CONCERNED ABOUT HIS MEMORY. I NEED HIM READY TO GO *TONIGHT!* WE'VE HAD ANOTHER VISIT TO MY OFFICE BY THAT COSTUMED *FREAK!* I WANT OVERT-KILL OPERATIONAL *A.S.A.P.!*

* SEE VIOLATOR MINI-SERIES, ISSUE 2 -- Tom.

HOPELESS.

THAT'S HOW TERRY FEELS AT THE MOMENT. IN HIS RUSH TO GET HOME TO SEE IF HIS FAMILY IS ALRIGHT, HE'D FORGOTTEN THAT TODAY IS WHEN WANDA AND THE BABY GO TO VISIT GRANDMA BLAKE.

NORMALLY.

HE HASN'T BEEN ABLE TO GET THEM ON THE PHONE.

MAYBE THEY DIDN'T **MAKE IT?** MAYBE THEY'RE IN TROUBLE **ALREADY?** QUESTIONS RACE WILDLY THROUGH HIS MIND. HE CURSES HIS GROWING **PARANOIA.** AS A TRAINED SECURITY OPERATIVE, HE EXPECTS BETTER OF HIMSELF.

BUT NO.

ONLY ONE THOUGHT REPEATS.

please. be okay. wanda.

AGAIN, HE LOOKS OUT THE WINDOW. AGAIN, HE SEES AN UNMARKED CAR WITH TWO C.I.A. STIFFS.

HE'D SPOTTED THEM ON HIS FRANTIC DRIVE HOME.

HIS PARANOIA IS OBVIOUSLY NOT UNFOUNDED.

THEY PARKED RIGHT OUT FRONT. IT'S OBVIOUS THEY WANT HIM TO KNOW HE'S BEING TOYED WITH.

FINALLY, THE GUNS FALL SILENT.

LISTEN UP, FITZGERALD!! I KNOW YOU CAN HEAR US!

WE'VE *GOT* YOUR *WIFE AND GIRL!* IF YOU WANT TO SEE *EITHER* OF THEM AGAIN, YOU BE IN THE ALLEY BETWEEN FIFTH AND SIXTH AT 27th--

--AT *MIDNIGHT!*

AND YOU'D BETTER BE *ALONE!*

TIRES SCREECH AS THE CAR SPEEDS AWAY.

IT'S AT THIS MOMENT THAT TERRY'S WORLD BECOMES DEVOID OF REALITY. HE ISN'T AWARE THAT THE MAFIA WISEGUYS WERE *LYING.* WANDA, CYAN AND GRANDMA BLAKE WERE ACTUALLY AT A PARK, QUIETLY OBSERVED BY SOME OF TWIST'S MEN. THEY CALLED THIS INFORMATION IN TO THE THUGS AT TERRY'S DOORSTEP, WHO WERE THEN TO PASS HIM THE BOGUS 'KIDNAP' STORY.

OF COURSE, TERRY WOULD IMMEDIATELY CHECK ON GRANDMA'S HOUSE.

OF COURSE, IT'D BE EMPTY.

THIS WOULD MAKE THE BLUFF THAT MUCH MORE *CONVINCING.*

WHAT THE MOBSTERS HADN'T FORSEEN WAS THE PRESENCE OF THE C.I.A.

THIS COMPLICATION WAS EASILY RESOLVED.

NOW, TERRY STANDS OVER THE TWO DEAD G-MEN. THE SECURITY AGENCIES HAD NOTHING BUT WYNN'S LIES TO FOLLOW UNTIL NOW. *NO WAY* THEY'LL BELIEVE A COUPLE OF HITMEN HAPPENED ALONG AND HAD A SHOOT-OUT ON HIS FRONT LAWN.

AS THE SOUND OF SIRENS DRAWS CLOSER, AND THE NEIGHBORS START TO PEEK THROUGH THEIR CURTAINS, TERRY DOES THE ONLY THING HE CAN THINK OF.

HE RUNS.

DAMMIT! WHERE'D I PUT 'EM?!

PANIC.

KUNK

FAASH

KRASH THMP

HE HAD BURIED THE TWO STEEL-PIERCING AK720/X1 PORTABLE CANNONS.

SPAWN KNEW THAT THEY MIGHT COME IN HANDY SOMEDAY, SO HE KEPT THE GUNS HIDDEN. ANYTHING SHARP, ROTTEN OR HEAVY ENOUGH TO DISCOURAGE IDLE CURIOSITY WAS USED AS CAMOUFLAGE.

THESE WEAPONS HAD DECIMATED OVER-KILL ON THEIR FIRST GO-ROUND. * THEY'LL WORK A SECOND TIME -- IF HE CAN FIND THEM.

ISSUE 7 -- Tom

SPAWN REALIZES THAT EACH PASSING MOMENT IS KEEPING TERRY IN A POTENTIALLY FATAL POSITION.

THERE'S NO TIME FOR DELAY...

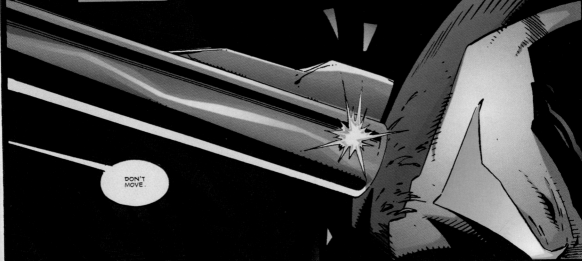

...ON ANY LEVEL.

DON'T MOVE.

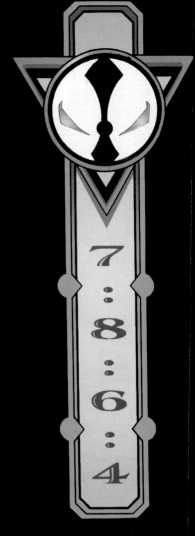

7
:
8
:
6
:
4

...AND TO HIS FRIENDS.

TO BE CONTINUED.

3

T H E   H U N T
P a r t   T h r e e

JASON WYNN: HEAD OF THE UNITED STATES SECURITY GROUP, THE HIGHEST-LEVEL INTELLIGENCE AGENCY.

HIS SECURITY STATUS HAS BEEN COMPROMISED, AND THE PRESIDENT'S OFFICE IS NOT PLEASED. WYNN IS UNDER PRESSURE TO RESTORE HIS REPUTATION IN THE INTELLIGENCE COMMUNITY. TERRY FITZGERALD, A VICTIM OF CIRCUMSTANCE, HAS BEEN IDENTIFIED AS THE SOURCE OF THE TENSION... AND IS NOW IN DANGER OF HIS LIFE, AT WYNN'S DIRECTION.

SPAWN: AGENT OF HELL.

HIS VERY EXISTENCE HAS SET INTO MOTION A CRAZY RIPPLE EFFECT, WITH INCREASINGLY DANGEROUS CONSEQUENCES FOR THOSE AROUND HIM. SPAWN SIMPLY WANTS TO CREATE AND NURTURE A FAMILY, BUT THAT DESIRE HAS ALREADY DAMNED HIM AND NOW INADVERTANTLY THREATENS ALL WHO TRUST HIM.

TONY TWIST: MAFIA DON.

HIS OPERATIONS HAD RUN SMOOTHLY FOR YEARS, BUT LATELY AN UNKNOWN ATTACKER HAS SLAUGHTERED A NUMBER OF HIS MEN. TWIST HAS FOCUSED ON REMOVING THIS BLEMISH... SPAWN, HE BELIEVES,... FROM THE FACE OF HIS CITY. HE IS UNAWARE THAT SOME OF THE INFORMATION DRIVING HIS HUNT IS INACCURATE.

WANDA BLAKE: WIDOW OF LT. COL. AL SIMMONS, A.K.A. SPAWN.

WANDA IS NOW HAPPILY MARRIED TO HER LATE HUSBAND'S BEST FRIEND, TERRY FITZGERALD, WITH WHOM SHE HAS A DAUGHTER, CYAN. SHE IS CURRENTLY UNAWARE OF AL'S LIFE STATUS, OR OF THE VICIOUS WEB IN WHICH TERRY IS RAPIDLY FINDING HIMSELF ENSNARED.

SAM BURKE: DETECTIVE, N.Y.P.D.

NOW CLEARED OF WRONGDOING IN THE DEATH OF CHILDKILLER BILLY KINCAID, BURKE IS ALLOWING HIMSELF THE LUXURY OF BRUTALITY IN THE NAME OF FACT GATHERING. SOMEONE (OR SOMETHING) CAUSED HIS SUPERIORS TO QUESTION HIS LOYALTY, AND HE WANTS TO HAVE WORDS WITH THIS INDIVIDUAL.

"TWITCH" WILLIAMS: DETECTIVE, N.Y.P.D.

THIS FATHER OF SEVEN IS ONE OF THE STATE'S TOP SHARPSHOOTERS. HIS SENSE OF FAIRNESS WORKS COUNTERPOINT TO HIS PARTNER BURKE'S OCCASIONAL LAPSES. METHODOLOGY AND ARM-TWISTING HAVE LED THE PAIR TO THEIR QUARRY-- THE COSTUMED MYSTERY MAN WHO HAS A FEW SERIOUS QUESTIONS TO ANSWER.

THESE ARE THE MAJOR PLAYERS IN AN INCREASINGLY TWISTED GAME OF CAT AND MOUSE. EACH IS SOMEHOW CONNECTED TO THE STRANGE EXISTENCE OF A *DEAD MAN* BROUGHT BACK TO *LIFE*. STRIPPED OF HIS IDENTITY... CHARGED WITH TREMENDOUS BUT EXHAUSTABLE *POWER*... AWAKENED FIVE YEARS AFTER HIS TIME TO FIND HIS WIFE REMARRIED... THESE WERE THE REALITIES AWAITING A MAN IN LOVE--

-- *GIFTS* GIVEN BY SOME UNHOLY *CREATURE OF HELL*.

A PRISONER OF HIS NEW LIFE ON EARTH, SPAWN'S ACTIONS HAVE TRIGGERED SEVERAL *MANHUNTS* BY VERY INFLUENCIAL PEOPLE. NONE IS PREPARED FOR WHAT *TRUTH* MAY EMERGE FROM THEIR INVESTIGATIONS...

TWITCH! **STOP HIM!**

KRAK!

DETECTIVE WILLIAMS LINES UP HIS TARGET. SPAWN'S CHAOTIC MOVEMENTS DON'T DISTRACT HIM. NOR DOES THE FLOWING CAPE WHICH CONCEALS MOST OF HIS FORM. "TWITCH" WAITS FOR JUST THE RIGHT MOMENT.

THE SHOT IS A DIRECT HIT. TEARING THROUGH CARTILAGE AND SHATTERING A KNEECAP, IT'S THE FASTEST WAY TO DISABLE AN ASSAILANT.

SPAWN NEVER BREAKS STRIDE AS HE DISAPPEARS INTO THE UNLIT ALLEYWAY.

TWITCH -- I THOUGHT YOU--

I DID, SIR!

I DID!

SHOCK.

THEN REALITY SETS BACK IN. SAM AND TWITCH DART AFTER THE FLEEING HERO.

JEEZ!

THIS IS GETTING NUTS!

*ISSUE 12 -- Tom·

TIRES SCREECH. A DOOR SNAPS OPEN. OUT BOLTS *WANDA BLAKE*.

DURING THE DRIVE HOME SHE WAS IN A NEAR FRENZY OVER WHAT SHE'D BEEN TOLD. MAYBE *THIS* PART WAS TRUE... OR THAT... OR THAT. BUT *TERRY...?* NO. SOMETHING *IS WRONG* HERE.

HEY LADY! MY *FARE!!*

MS. BLAKE!

MS. BLAKE!!

AS SHE NEARS THE CLUSTER OF POLICE, REPORTERS AND GAWKERS HER *HEART* SKIPS A BEAT, THEN CONTINUES TO POUND LIKE IT'S ABOUT TO *EXPLODE*.

IS IT TRUE YOUR HUSBAND KILLED

F.B.I.

TRAITOR

FLED THE SCENE

MURDER

SHE'S ASSAULTED WITH A HUNDRED QUESTIONS AND THIRTY VERSIONS OF THE EVENTS. SIMULTANEOUSLY.

EXCUSE ME, FOLKS, LET ME PASS.

MS. BLAKE!

MS. BLAKE!

I'M SORRY, MA'AM. THINGS DON'T LOOK GOOD RIGHT NOW. I'M GOING TO NEED YOU TO COME DOWN TO THE STATION.

THERE'S BEEN A MULTIPLE MURDER, AND NO SIGN OF YOUR HUSBAND. WE'VE PUT OUT AN A.P.B. CALLING FOR HIS ARREST...

NO!

PLEASE!

NOT *TERRY!*

NOT MY *TERRY!*

IT *CAN'T* BE!

SPOTTING A HANDFUL OF NEIGHBORS HUDDLED ACROSS THE STREET, WANDA RACES TO THEM.

PLEASE!

YOU *MUST* HAVE SEEN SOMETHING! ANYTHING!

PLEASE, YOU'VE GOT TO HELP. THIS *CAN'T* BE TRUE!

THIS CAN'T BE TRUE.

MR. HORNE?

ANNE?

WE'VE SEEN NOTHING.

I'M SORRY.

WANDA IS FAR TOO LATE. JASON WYNN'S MEN HAD ALREADY "*CONSULTED*" WITH HER NEIGHBORS.

YOU SEE, ANDREW AND KAREN HORNE THESE KIND AND GENEROUS PEOPLE, WERE *ILLEGAL IMMIGRANTS*.

AN INSURANCE ADJUSTER FOR OVER SEVENTEEN YEARS, CHRIS ALBRECHT LED A FAIRLY MUNDANE LIFE.

FOR THREE YEARS IN THE MID-SEVENTIES, THOUGH, HE DIDN'T FILE HIS *INCOME TAX* FORMS. AN AUDIT AT THIS TIME WOULD RUIN HIM.

AS FOR ANNE THOMOPOULOS, SHE HAS ALWAYS BEEN A PLEASANT NEIGHBOR. NICE FAMILY, TOO. BUT SHE HAS A SKELETON IN HER CLOSET.

SHE HAD A CHILD OUT OF WEDLOCK-- A SON-- WHEN SHE WAS SEVENTEEN. AT PRESENT HE IS IN JAIL FOR CAR THEFT. HIS PAROLE HEARING IS IN TWO MONTHS. SHE'S BEEN PROMISED HIS FREEDOM.

AS THE FINAL DOOR IS LATCHED,
SHE FALLS TO HER KNEES,
SOBBING.

WANDA NEVER WANTED TO ADMIT IT TO HERSELF, BUT SHE ALWAYS **KNEW** THIS
DAY WOULD COME. BEING A WIDOW TO ONE GOVERNMENT INTELLIGENCE AGENT
WASN'T ENOUGH, SHE HAD TO GO MARRY **ANOTHER**. SHE'D ACTED AS IF, BY KEEPING
A SAFE DISTANCE FROM THEIR WORK, SHE WOULD SHIELD THEM ALL FROM ANY
CONSEQUENCES OF... WELL, WHATEVER THAT WORK **WAS**. "IGNORANCE IS BLISS,"
SHE'D TOLD HERSELF.

THAT ILLUSION HAS JUST BEEN SHATTERED... **TERMINALLY**. WANDA KNOWS SHE'D'VE
SEEN WARNING LIGHTS FLASHING IF ONLY SHE'D OPENED HER EYES A BIT WIDER.

SHE SAYS A QUICK
PRAYER FOR HER CHILD,
WHO'S BEEN LEFT...
THANK GOD...
AT GRANNY BLAKE'S.

THEN, SHE BREAKS DOWN **AGAIN**,
HER BODY JERKING WITH EACH BREATH.

TRAGICALLY, HER PRIVACY IS
SHORT-LIVED AS THE ASSEMBLED
NEWSHOUNDS POUNCE,
FEEDING ON HER GRIEF.

MEANWHILE...

NO. I CAN'T
JUST LEAVE
HIM.

HE SAVED
≥ungh≤
MY
LIFE!

WAVES OF PAIN SHOOTING THROUGH
HIS BODY, TERRY MANAGES TO PUSH AN
EMPTY DUMPSTER DOWN THE ALLEY.

HE WON'T ABANDON
THE COSTUMED
VIGILANTE.

WITH EACH
AGONIZING
STEP,
MOMENTUM
IS BUILT--

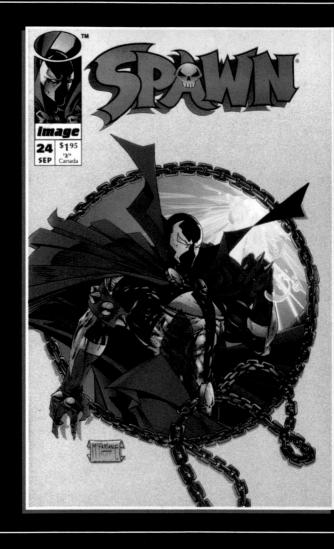

IT'S BEEN A VERY STRANGE NIGHT FOR *DETECTIVE SAM BURKE.* WHILE HUNTING THE MYSTERIOUS COSTUMED VIGILANTE RESPONSIBLE FOR BURKE'S TEMPORARY SUSPENSION FROM THE POLICE FORCE, BURKE AND HIS PARTNER-- *"TWITCH" WILLIAMS--* UNEXPECTEDLY FOUND THEMSELVES IN THE MIDDLE OF A MUCH BIGGER SCENARIO.

VARIOUS SOURCES LED THEM TO THE LAIR OF A HERO REVERED BY THE HOMELESS OF NEW YORK'S *BOWERY.* THEY CAUGHT HIM OFF-GUARD AS HE PREPARED FOR A SHOWDOWN TWO MILES UPTOWN WITH THE MAFIA'S CYBORG HITMAN, *OVERTKILL.* SPAWN EVADED THE PURSUIT.

THE LAWMEN LATER CAUGHT UP WITH SPAWN AS HIS BATTLE REACHED ITS CLIMAX. WILLIAMS' SHARPSHOOTING SAVED SPAWN'S LIFE-- AND THAT OF ONE OTHER. ALSO LYING IN A BLOODY HEAP WAS AN UNIDENTIFIED CIVILIAN.

AS BURKE STARES DOWN AT THE TWO BROKEN FIGURES, HE MUTTERS HIS PROFES- SIONAL ASSESSMENT:

CRIPES! THE PAPERWORK ON THIS IS GONNA *KILL* ME.

SO IT WOULD SEEM, SIR.

IT'S OBVIOUS THAT HE'S NOT EVEN REMOTELY AWARE OF THE MAGNITUDE OF WHAT'S JUST HAPPENED.

HE'LL CATCH ON SOON ENOUGH.

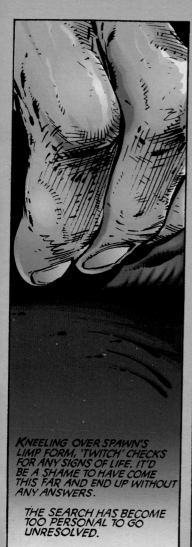

KNEELING OVER SPAWN'S LIMP FORM, 'TWITCH' CHECKS FOR ANY SIGNS OF LIFE. IT'D BE A SHAME TO HAVE COME THIS FAR AND END UP WITHOUT ANY ANSWERS.

THE SEARCH HAS BECOME TOO PERSONAL TO GO UNRESOLVED.

SO... WHAT'S THE SCOOP?

HE MIGHT BE DEAD.

I'M NOT FINDING A PULSE.

I'LL TRY SOME C.P.R.

THE MASK IS DRAWN BACK, REVEALING WHAT'S LEFT OF THE MAN CALLED AL SIMMONS.

JEEEZUS!!

WHAT THE HELL HAPPENED TO HIM?!

MY GOD.

JASON WYNN HAS BECOME CONSUMED WITH THIS CASE.

HIS FAUX PAS OVER TERRY FITZGERALD THREATENS HIS CAREER.

AND... IF HE SO MUCH AS LOOKS AT YOU CROSSEYED, MAKE SURE HIS *DEATH* LOOKS LIKE AN *ACCIDENT.*

DO YOU READ ME?

PERFECTLY, SIR.

HE *KNOWS* FITZGERALD IS NO TRAITOR, BUT CIRCUMSTANCES MADE HIM THE *LOGICAL* SUSPECT. RATHER THAN ADMIT HIS ERROR, WYNN CONTINUES TO CONDUCT A BRUTAL INVESTIGATION.

POLICE, F.B.I. ... ALL ARE CALLED INTO PLAY.

ANYTHING ELSE?

JUST DO IT.

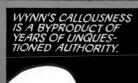

WYNN'S CALLOUSNESS IS A BYPRODUCT OF YEARS OF UNQUESTIONED AUTHORITY.

AS SUPREME DIRECTOR OF U.S. INTELLIGENCE AGENCIES, HE HAS SINGLE-HANDEDLY ENDED WARS... EVEN SOME HE BEGAN.

TERRY FITZGERALD IS ONLY *ONE MAN.* HIS LIFE MEANS *NOTHING* TO A DICTATOR WHOSE EFFECTIVENESS IS BEING QUESTIONED.

A QUICK RESOLUTION TO THIS FIASCO WILL RESTORE HIS PREEMINANCE WITH THE WHITE HOUSE, AND IN THE *GLOBAL COMMUNITY...*

...WHILE LEAVING IT TO OTHERS TO DEAL WITH ITS AFTERMATH...

...LIKE WANDA BLAKE, WIFE OF A MAN NOW ACCUSED ALSO OF MURDERING TWO F.B.I. AGENTS.

TEARS FALL AS SHE PRAYS THAT THIS IS JUST SOME DEMENTED *NIGHTMARE...* BUT SHE KNOWS THAT IT'S REAL.

VERY REAL.

THE LIFE SHE AND TERRY HAD BUILT HAS CRASHED DOWN AROUND HER. AS WANDA NOW HOLDS TIGHT TO HER DAUGHTER CYAN, SHE WORKS TO PUSH PAST THE SHOCK... TO FOCUS ON WHAT'S IN HER HEART:

HOPE.
LOVE.

SHE PRAYS TO GOD THAT THIS WILL BE ENOUGH TO SEE HER THROUGH...

...BECAUSE IT SEEMS NOTHING SHE TOOK FOR GRANTED CAN BE TRUSTED.

THE AGENTS POSTED OUTSIDE ARE SUPPOSEDLY THERE TO *PROTECT* HER... BUT FROM *WHO?* OR IS SHE BEING *DETAINED?* THE NEIGHBORS STOPPED TALKING TO HER AFTER THE SHOOTOUT. WHO WERE THEY *AFRAID* OF?

WHAT WAS TERRY INVOLVED IN?

SHE DOESN'T KNOW FRIEND FROM FOE.

"...HOW MANY TIMES DO I HAVE TO TELL YOU-- I DON'T *KNOW* WHERE THAT FRIGGIN' ROBOT WENT.*

YOUR GUESS IS AS GOOD AS MINE. I WAS JUST TRYING TO STAY *ALIVE*.

I WAS EXPECTING TO BE MEETING HERE WITH A COUPLE OF MAFIA PUNKS.

*WE DO. SEE YOUNGBLOOD #7 -- Tom-

YEAH YEAH. LET'S SEE IF I GOT THIS STRAIGHT... YOU'RE A G-MAN WHO'S EXPECTING A MEETING WITH THE MOB. THEY *SUCKER* YOU, SEND THEIR TEN-TON CYBORG HITMAN INSTEAD.

AND...

...OUR *DEAD HERO* OVER THERE SEEMS TO HAVE A *PERSONAL* REASON TO TRY AND SAVE YOUR BUTT.

ALL OF THIS COMES AS A *COMPLETE* SURPRISE TO YOU.

ON TOP OF IT ALL, YOU CLAIM TO HAVE LOST ALL YOUR IDENTIFI-CATION.

WHADDYA THINK, TWITCH?

THERE DOES SEEM TO BE SOME MERIT TO WHAT HE'S SAYING, SIR.

HE KNOWS THE AGENCY PROTOCOLS AND A FAIR BIT ABOUT THE MAFIA, AS WELL...

WILL YOU SHUT *UP*, TWITCH.

Psst! VINNIE! LOOK-- IT'S *AL!* SOMEONE MESSED HIM UP.

REAL *BAD*.

WE'VE GOTTA GET SOME HELP.

SO, ANOTHER GROUP IS DRAWN INTO THE WEB OF ACTIVITY SURROUNDING SPAWN, BECAUSE OUR NAIVE HERO ACTED WITHOUT THOUGHT OF CONSEQUENCE.

A DEAD CHILD MOLESTER.

A FEW STOLEN GUNS.

A COUPLE OF MISSING FILES.

THESE EVENTS FORM NO OBVIOUS PATTERN. THE KEY LIES IN AN UNFATHOMABLE PLACE:

IN THE SPRAWLING OFFICE OF NEW YORK MAFIA CHIEF ANTHONY TWISTELLI, TENSIONS ARE RUNNING HIGH. THOUGH HE LIVED THROUGH HIS ORDEAL WITH THE *VIOLATOR* AND HIS BROTHER DEMONS*, IT ENDED FAR FROM SATISFACTORILY.

AND NOW THE HEAT'S BEEN TURNED UP. TWO OF HIS BOYS, TAKEN BY SURPRISE, SHOT AND KILLED A PAIR OF FEDERAL AGENTS ON THE FRONT LAWN OF TERRY FITZGERALD'S HOUSE.

OUT OF RESPECT FOR EACH OTHERS' INFLUENCE, THE TWO GROUPS HAVE LONG HAD A "SPECIAL" WORKING RELATIONSHIP. TWIST IS LUCKY THAT EVERYONE IS STILL BLAMING FITZGERALD.

HE CAN THANK *JASON WYNN* FOR THAT.

YES?

THIS IS GINO. WE'VE JUST CALLED A MEETING FOR NEXT THURSDAY. SOME OF THE MEMBERS HAVE RE-QUESTED A PROGRESS REPORT. THERE'S BEEN UNHAPPINESS WITH YOUR RECENT DEALINGS

YOU'VE GOT SIX DAYS TO CORRECT THIS, UNDER-STAND?

WE'RE COUNTING ON YOU, TONY.

CLICK

I SENT FRANKIE AND TOMMY BACK TO THE MURDER SCENE.

THEY'RE MAKING SURE WE STAY CLEAN THROUGH ALL THIS.

AND US?

RING RING

I WANT YOU TO MAKE SURE *OVERTKILL* DID HIS JOB. I NEED FITZGERALD *DEAD.* THE CARTEL HAS BEEN--

RING RING

*VIOLATOR MINI-SERIES.– Tom.

PERFECT!!

TWIST IS NOT USED TO BEING ON THE RECEIVING END OF THREATS.

NOR WILL HE ALLOW IT TO CONTINUE.

SLAM!

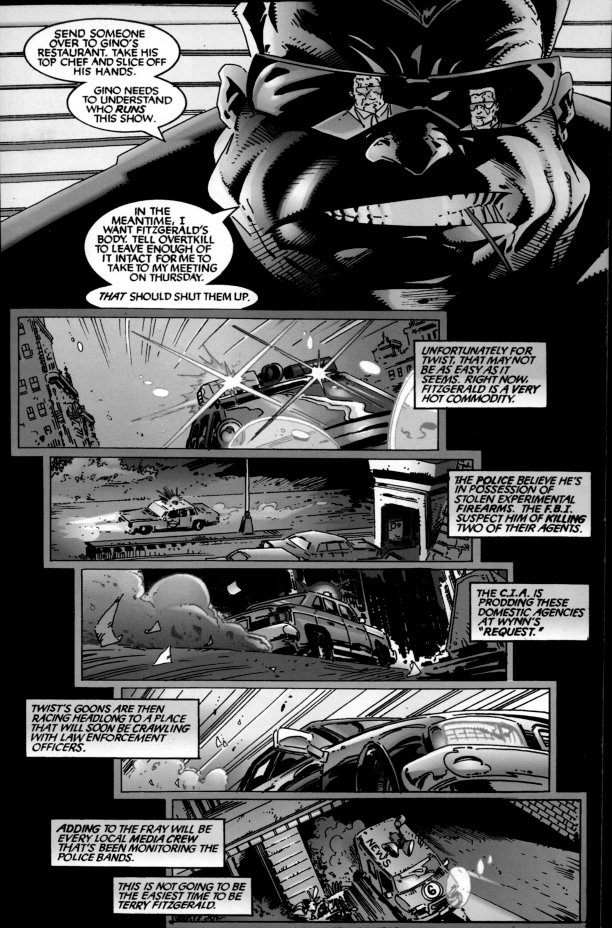

SEND SOMEONE OVER TO GINO'S RESTAURANT. TAKE HIS TOP CHEF AND SLICE OFF HIS HANDS.

GINO NEEDS TO UNDERSTAND WHO *RUNS* THIS SHOW.

IN THE MEANTIME, I WANT FITZGERALD'S BODY. TELL OVERTKILL TO LEAVE ENOUGH OF IT INTACT FOR ME TO TAKE TO MY MEETING ON THURSDAY.

THAT SHOULD SHUT THEM UP.

UNFORTUNATELY FOR TWIST, THAT MAY NOT BE AS EASY AS IT SEEMS. RIGHT NOW, FITZGERALD IS A VERY HOT COMMODITY.

THE POLICE BELIEVE HE'S IN POSSESSION OF STOLEN EXPERIMENTAL FIREARMS. THE F.B.I. SUSPECT HIM OF *KILLING* TWO OF THEIR AGENTS.

THE C.I.A. IS PRODDING THESE DOMESTIC AGENCIES AT WYNN'S "REQUEST."

TWIST'S GOONS ARE THEN RACING HEADLONG TO A PLACE THAT WILL SOON BE CRAWLING WITH LAW ENFORCEMENT OFFICERS.

ADDING TO THE FRAY WILL BE EVERY LOCAL MEDIA CREW THAT'S BEEN MONITORING THE POLICE BANDS.

THIS IS NOT GOING TO BE THE EASIEST TIME TO BE TERRY FITZGERALD.

THOUGH DETECTIVE SAM BURKE HAS HAD A VERY SUCCESSFUL CAREER, ONE POINT CANNOT BE DENIED: HE'S AN OVERWEIGHT SLOB.

FOR HIM, "PURSUING A SUSPECT ON FOOT" IS A CONTRADICTION IN TERMS. THAT'S WHY HE WAS TEAMED WITH SCRAWNY "TWITCH" WILLIAMS...

...TO WHOM IT FALLS (YET AGAIN) TO CATCH UP WITH A FLEEING PERPETPATOR (ALLEGED).

PRECINCT BY PRECINCT, THE QUESTION HAS BEEN ASKED, "WHY DO THEY CALL HIM 'TWITCH'?"

puff

THE ANSWER:

"BECAUSE HE DOESN'T!"

IT'S OVER, TERRY.

ACCEPT IT.

TERRY SLUMPS TO THE GROUND, A BROKEN MAN. PUTTING HIS HEAD INTO HIS HANDS, HE BEGINS TO SOB. HE DOESN'T KNOW WHY ANY OF THIS IS HAPPENING. THINGS ARE SO OUT OF WHACK.

BUT EVEN MORE IMPORTANTLY, HE HAS FAILED HIS WIFE AND CHILD. THAT IS MORE THAN HE CAN BEAR.

WANDA, PLEASE FORGIVE ME.

puff
puff

YOU huff GOT 'IM! GREAT... WORK...! huff-ff

I... THOUGHT I WAS GOING TO HAVE huff A HEART ATTACK...

GOOD FOR YOU, SIR.

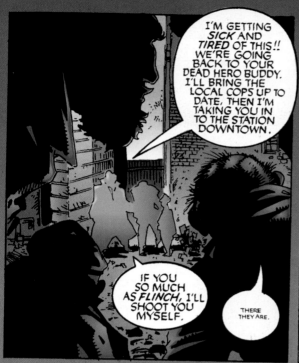

I'M GETTING *SICK* AND *TIRED* OF THIS!! WE'RE GOING BACK TO YOUR *DEAD HERO* BUDDY. I'LL BRING THE LOCAL COPS UP TO DATE, THEN I'M TAKING YOU IN TO THE STATION DOWNTOWN.

IF YOU SO MUCH AS *FLINCH*, I'LL SHOOT YOU MYSELF.

THERE THEY ARE.

KUNK!

HEY!

GET OUT OF HERE! GET OUT OF OUR ALLEY! *OUT OF OUR ALLEY!*

THEY STAND POISED IN THE MOONLIGHT, READY TO TAKE BACK WHAT IS THEIRS-- READY TO DEFEND THEIR FALLEN KING: *SPAWN.*

CANS. BOTTLES. WOOD. WHATEVER. THEY PELT THE TWO DETECTIVES RELENTLESSLY. TERRY SEES ANOTHER OPPORTUNITY TO FLEE.

NOW DISTANCED FROM THE POLICE, HE'S SPOTTED BY THE FIRST GROUP ON THE SCENE-- *THE C.I.A.*

SAY GOODNIGHT, TRAITOR.

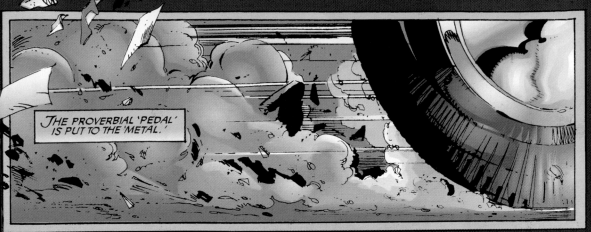

The proverbial 'pedal' is put to the 'metal.'

SIR, WE NEED TO FALL BACK!

I KNOW! I KNOW!

YOU GRAB FITZY! I'LL COVER YOU!

EVERYONE'S GOING *CRAZY* TONIGHT!

TERRY TURNS TO RUN.

TOO LATE.

HE STANDS FROZEN, STARING AT THE HEAD-LIGHTS LIKE SOME WILD ANIMAL ON THE HIGHWAY.

HE KNOWS HIS LUCK HAS FINALLY RUN OUT.

AS THE HORDE CONVERGES UPON HIM, SPAWN STANDS AND STARES. HIS C.I.A. BACKGROUND INFORMS HIS DECISIONS: WHEN TO REACT, AND HOW. HE HAS SEVERAL TARGETS TONIGHT. ONE PURPOSE.

UNTIL NOW, HE TRIED HIDING HIMSELF FROM THE PUBLIC.

THAT HASN'T WORKED VERY WELL.

FEAR.

IT CAN BE BROUGHT ON IN MANY WAYS: IRRATIONAL THOUGHT. PARANOIA. SUPER-STITION.

HE'S BEEN GIVEN A NAME BY THE VIOLATOR. IT'S TIME THEY LEARNED IT...

IT CAN ALSO BE INSTITUTED BY EXAMPLE.

HE NEEDS A NEW TACTIC:

...AS WELL AS SOMETHING ELSE:

THESE ALLEYS BELONG TO SPAWN

CRIPES. WHAT A NIGHT.

...THAT THE BOOGIE MAN REALLY DOES EXIST.

WHERE'D HE GO?

HE'S GOING TO MAKE SURE EVERYONE GETS THAT MESSAGE.

WITH VARIOUS FILES TAKEN FROM TONY TWIST'S OFFICE, SPAWN HAD BEGUN TO PIECE THINGS TOGETHER. EACH NEW AGENCY DROPPING INTO THE MIX WAS TARGETED AS ANOTHER PLACE FOR AL TO CROSS-CHECK HIS DATA.

FINALLY, ALL THAT REMAINED WAS TO ACT AS COURIER.

I'VE ALWAYS BEEN AMAZED HOW RELAXED YOU ARE ABOUT DESTROYING PEOPLE.

uh?

SHUT UP.

I'VE SOMETHING TO SAY.

YOU CALL YOUR DOGS OFF THE FITZGERALD CASE. THEN YOU BACKTRACK OVER THAT TWISTED TRAIL OF LIES YOU'VE LAID AND SOMEHOW YOU CORRECT IT. I WANT TERRY FITZGERALD TO BE SO SQUEAKY CLEAN THEY'LL WANT TO GIVE HIM A MEDAL. IN THE FUTURE, YOU AND YOUR PEOPLE WILL STAY AWAY FROM HIM AND HIS FAMILY.

IN CASE I HAVEN'T MADE MY POINT, I THOUGHT I'D LEAVE YOU WITH A COPY OF A SPECIAL FILE.

YOU'LL FIND THAT YOUR CAREER OF WEALTH AND POWER WILL VANISH IF ANYONE READS IT. THE PRESIDENT AND THE JOINT CHIEFS OF STAFF WOULD BE THE FIRST.

I KNOW WHAT MAKES YOU TICK, JASON...

WHA...? HOW'D YOU...!

...AND THAT'S POWER.

THIS FILE CAN MAKE IT DISAPPEAR IN A HEARTBEAT.

WYNN

JASON WYNN SCANS THE FILE. NO ONE ALIVE KNEW SOME OF THE ITEMS IT CONTAINS.

AT THE HOME OF TERRY FITZGERALD AND HIS WIFE, WANDA BLAKE, THE EFFECTS OF SPAWN'S CRYPTIC VISITS ARE DISCUSSED IN HUSHED TONES.

IT JUST DOESN'T MAKE ANY *SENSE* TO ME. NONE OF THIS.

I'VE GOT THE ENTIRE *CITY* CHASING ME DOWN, TRYING TO *NAIL* ME. THEN, JUST WHEN THEY'VE GOT ME... *BAM,* I'M FREE TO GO.

RIGHT IN THE MIDDLE OF THEIR *INTERROGATION, SOMEONE* WHISPERS *SOMETHING* IN THEIR EAR, AND I BECOME A *NON-ISSUE.*

HONEY, I DON'T PRETEND TO KNOW WHAT THIS IS ALL ABOUT, BUT IT *SCARED* ME. ALL I COULD THINK OF WAS LOSING YOU, OF CYAN NOT HAVING A DADDY. OF YOU NOT SEEING HER *GROW UP.*

I COULDN'T BEAR THAT.

I WAS SCARED, TOO, SWEETHEART. I STILL AM.

SOMEONE MESSED WITH OUR LIVES. THEN, JUST LIKE THAT, IT'S ALL CALLED OFF. IT TAKES AN *AWFUL* LOT OF INFLUENCE TO DO SOMETHING LIKE THAT.

THAT SCARES ME.

OUTSIDE, IN THE COLD NIGHT AIR, OUR HERO PERCHES HIGH ABOVE HIS WIFE'S HOUSE.

HIS HOUSE.

OR IS IT.

HIS LIFE IS SO TWISTED NOW, HE CAN'T MAKE SENSE OF IT.

WHILE HE STARES AT THE LIGHT STREAMING FROM THE HOUSE THAT WAS ONCE HIS, AL SIMMONS REFLECTS THAT HIS EXISTENCE IS CERTAINLY HAVING AN IMPACT-- AND THAT MOST OF IT'S NEGATIVE.

HE'LL BE MORE CAREFUL IN THE FUTURE. HIS ACTIONS HAVE CAUSED HIS WIFE AND FRIEND TO SUFFER GREATLY.

SOUNDS FUNNY, HE THINKS, I HAVE A WIFE THAT'S MARRIED TO SOMEONE ELSE.

HE'LL LAUGH ABOUT THAT SOME OTHER TIME.

FOR NOW, A DISASTER HAS BEEN AVERTED.

AS THE FIRST OF THE RAIN BEGINS TO FALL, HE DOES ALLOW HIMSELF A SLIGHT SMIRK.

HIS BLUFFS HAVE WORKED.

HE'LL WORRY ABOUT EVERYTHING ELSE TOMORROW.

The END.

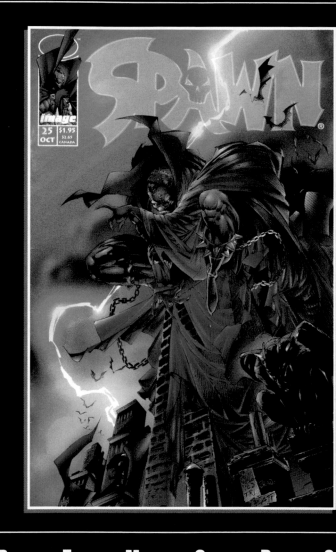

...AND POLICE IN QUEENS STILL HAVE NO COMMENT ON THE DEATHS THERE OF TWO F.B.I. AGENTS LAST WEEK.

IN NEW YORK'S BOWERY, MEANWHILE, THERE HAVE BEEN REPORTS OF GANG-RELATED COMBAT AGAINST A COSTUMED META-BEING. A MELEE INVOLVING POLICE DETECTIVES, A GOVERNMENT EMPLOYEE, A TECHNO-AUGMENTED MERCENARY, AND THIS PREVIOUSLY UNKNOWN HERO WAS OBSERVED BY LOCAL NEWS CREWS. BIOLUMINESCENT GRAPHITTI WAS THEN DISCOVERED IDENTIFYING THE NEW-COMER AS "SPAWN." POLICE BELIEVE HE MAY BE LINKED WITH THE VIGILANTE MURDERS OF KNOWN CRIME LORDS SEVERAL MONTHS AGO.

WELL, WELL. IF IT ISN'T RATINGS WAR TIME IN THE BROADCAST NEWS INDUSTRY, WHAT TIME *IS* IT? NEW YORK CITY, HQ TO RADIO AND TELEVISION AND THE HOME OF BROADWAY, HAS NOW PREMIERED A PERFORMANCE OF ANOTHER KIND. THE BIG APPLE IS NOW PLAYING HOST TO THE MOST OUTLANDISH SCENES OF CARNAGE THIS SIDE OF BOSNIA--IF YOU BELIEVE THE NEWS FOLKS. WHAT DO YOU GET WHEN YOU MIX CYBORG WARRIORS, THE F.B.I., THE C.I.A. AND THE COPS-- *PLUS* A MAGICAL VIGILANTE--FIGHTING ALL OVER TOWN? *DOUBLE DIGIT NIELSENS!* AND THEY DISMISS *MY* CHANNEL AS LOWBROW INFOTAINMENT!

EITHER *HELL* HAS FROZEN OVER OR IT'S FINALLY *MY* TURN TO SEE SOME JUSTICE IN THIS WORLD. THERE'S NOW APPEARED A COSTUMED DO-GOODER *I* CAN BELIEVE IN. IF HE IS THE VIGILANTE--AND HE'S DEFINITELY SHOWING ENOUGH BRASS-- THEN *GOD BLESS* THIS SPAWN, WHO-EVER HE IS. WE'VE *NEEDED* SOMEONE TO STAND UP AND CLEAR OUR CITY OF ALL THE SMUG SELF-INTERESTED FILTH. MIX EQUAL DOSES OF MOB-BASHING AND GOVERNMENT-SMASHING AND YOU'VE GOT *MY KIND OF HERO.* SO, SPAWN, WHOEVER YOU ARE, *WHAT*EVER YOU ARE, IF YOU CAN HEAR THIS...

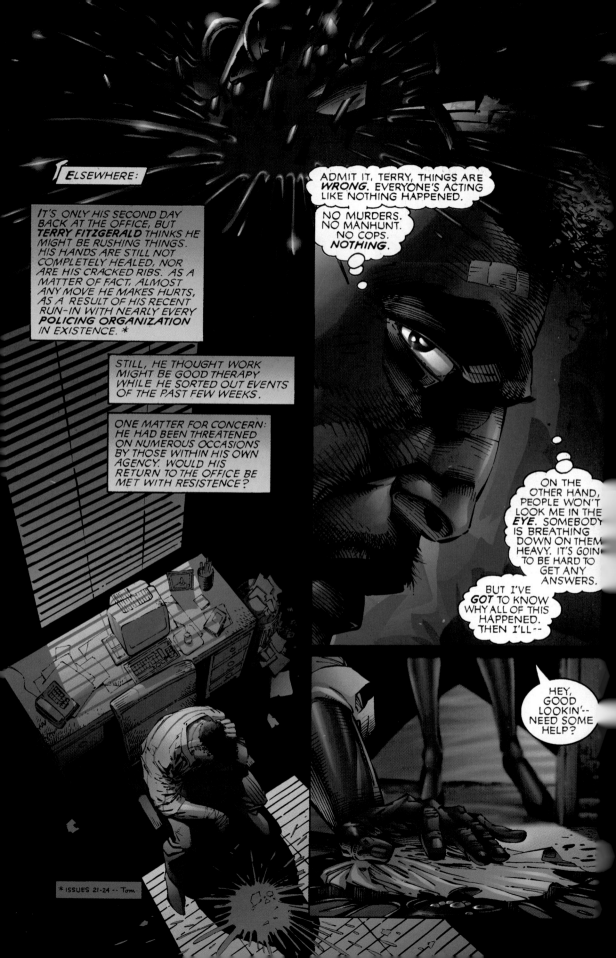

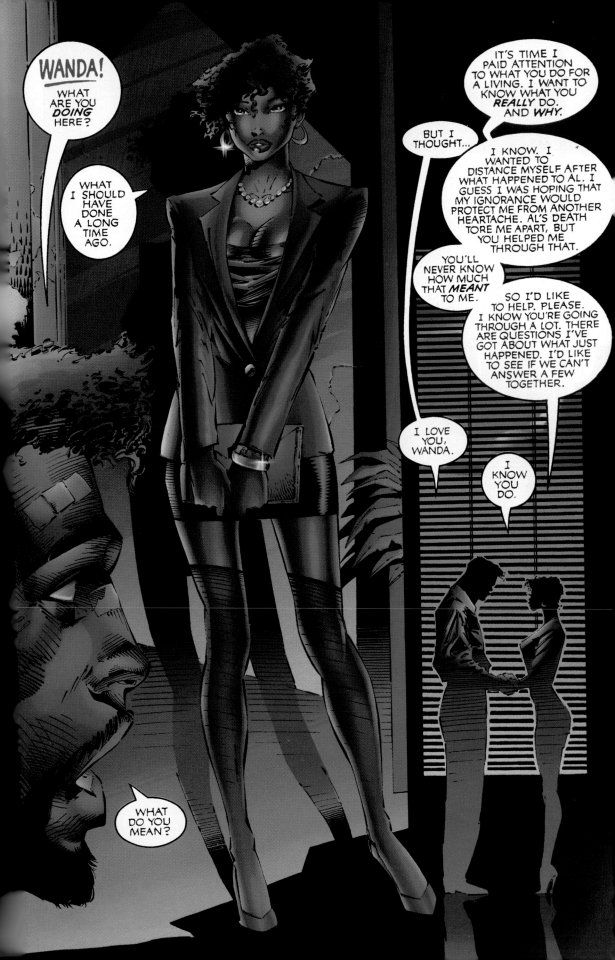

DRY, ROTTING BOARDS SHATTER AFTER A QUICK FORCEFUL KICK. THIS DENIZEN OF THE SHADOW-LANDS IS ANXIOUS TO BRAG TO HIS LEADER. TELL HIM THAT HE'S DONE HIS DUTY.

AS A GRUNT IN 'CHARLIE' COMPANY IN VIETNAM, *DAVID BREWI* THRIVED. NOW, NEARLY TWO DECADES LATER, *THE* SHELL-SHOCKED VET CARRIES ON THE LIFESTYLE OF A WAR LONG OVER.

BOSS! YOU IN HERE?

THERE YOU ARE.

I PROCEEDED INTO SECTOR 12, LIKE YOU SAID. INFORMED THE ENEMY OF OUR STATUS AND REQUESTED THEIR IMMEDIATE WITHDRAWAL.

I ALSO MADE THREATS AND SLAPPED HIM UP A BIT.

THEY SEEM VERY LOYAL TO THEIR COMMANDER. HE'S OBVIOUSLY GIVEN THEM A FALSE SENSE OF SECURITY.

YOU'VE DONE WELL, DAVID.

SPAWN.

HE'S **ACCEPTED** THE NAME.
OUT OF **NECESSITY**.

HIS NEW TITLE IS, FOR THE FIRST TIME, PUBLIC
KNOWLEDGE. HE HAD TRIED TO AVOID CONTACT
WITH THE 'REAL' WORLD, INSTEAD BIDING HIS TIME
IN THE SHADOWS OF MANHATTAN'S BACK STREETS.

THAT DIDN'T WORK.

ALL HE WANTED WAS TO SEE HIS
WIFE. TO RETURN TO HIS ONE
TRUE LOVE. INSTEAD, HE'S
BEEN **HUNTED**. A DEAD
MAN FROM HELL
DOES NOT PASS
UNNOTICED.

SO, INSTEAD OF
RECAPTURING HIS PAST
LIFE, HE'S MERELY BEEN
AVOIDING IT, LOOKING
TO SOLVE THE UNWANTED
SITUATIONS THAT HAVE
FOLLOWED HIM INTO
THE ALLEYS.

NOW, THAT HAS **BACKFIRED**.

HE BROUGHT UNDUE **HARM** TO HIS
WIFE THROUGH HIS OWN CARELESS
ACTIONS. RATHER THAN BEING
PROTECTED, SHE WAS ALMOST
KILLED.*

HE WON'T ALLOW THAT AGAIN.

*SEE RECENT
ISSUES -- Tom.

THE AIR BEGINS TO THICKEN AS THE EARLY MORNING HOURS PASS AWAY.

HE CAME HERE TO REST. TO THINK.

SO HE **MUST** SEIZE THOSE MOMENTS.

HE IS NOW SOMETHING **DIFFERENT**. SOMETHING DARK AND FOUL AND **DISGUSTING**.

DEFEND HIS BELIEFS. ACT LIKE A MAN.

IN HIS FORMER LIFE HE FOUGHT AND KILLED FOR WHAT HE BELIEVED IN. BUT THAT WAS **ANOTHER** AL SIMMONS, HE TELLS HIMSELF.

AS HE STARES DOWN AT SCATTERED GROUPS OF HOMELESS PEOPLE, HE KNOWS THAT HIS MOMENTS OF FEELING HUMAN HAVE BECOME **RARE**.